Book

C

My Spelling Workbook

This book belongs to:

nobody

Includes CD
'Interactive Spelling Activities'

Prim-Ed
Publishing

www.prim-ed.com

My Spelling Workbook *(Book C)*

Published by Prim-Ed Publishing 2011

Copyright© Prim-Ed Publishing 2011

ISBN 978-1-84654-191-9

PR–2282

Titles available in this series:
My Spelling Workbook *(Book A)*
My Spelling Workbook *(Book B)*
My Spelling Workbook *(Book C)*
My Spelling Workbook *(Book D)*
My Spelling Workbook *(Book E)*
My Spelling Workbook *(Book F)*
My Spelling Workbook *(Book G)*

Offices in:

UK and Republic of Ireland:
Bosheen
New Ross
County Wexford
www.prim-ed.com

Australia:
PO Box 332
Greenwood
Western Australia 6924
www.ricpublications.com.au

Introduction

Welcome to *My Spelling Workbook and CD*.

This book and CD have lots of activities to help you learn to spell.

You should follow this method when you are learning to spell each word.

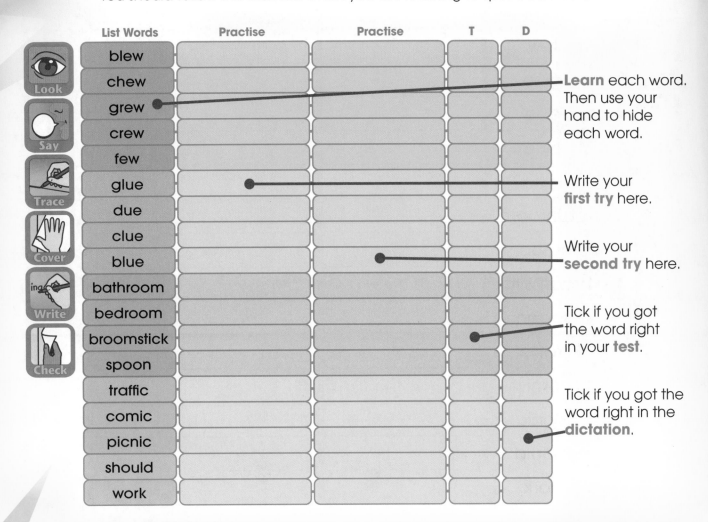

Contents

Unit 1 *ew, ue, oo, ic* 2–5

Unit 2 *o saying u, -ck* 6–9

Unit 3 *nk, i-e, y, ie, igh* 10–13

Unit 4 *ll, ss, zz, ff* 14–17

Unit 5 *le* 18–21

Unit 6 *scr, spr, str* 22–25

Unit 7 *Christmas* 26–29

Unit 8 *qu, squ* 30–33

Unit 9 *old, ind* 34–37

Unit 10 *ice, ace* 38–41

Unit 11 *ge, dge, ch, tch* 42–45

Unit 12 *Compound Words* 46–49

Unit 13 *Spring/Easter* 50–53

Unit 14 *Contractions* 54–57

Unit 15 *aw, oa, ore, a* 58–61

Unit 16 *war* 62–65

Unit 17 *Silent Letters* 66–69

Unit 18 *Summer Holidays* 70–73

Difficult Words I Have Found 74

My Spelling Dictionary Aa–Zz 75–78

Unit 1

ew   ue   oo   ic

 Look

 Say

 Trace

 Cover

 Write

 Check

List Words	Practise	Practise	T	D
blew				
chew				
grew				
crew	crew			
few				
glue				
due				
clue				
blue				
bathroom				
bedroom				
broomstick				
spoon				
traffic				
comic				
picnic				
should				
work				

 Picture Matching

1. Write the list word that matches each picture.

(a) _____

(b) _____

(c) _____

(d) _____

 Missing Letters

2. Complete these list words.

(a) br _ _ mst _ ck

(b) _ _ _ ff _ _

(c) _ e _

(d) sh _ _ _ _ d

(e) s _ o _ n

(f) b _ t _ _ _ om

Crossword

3. Use list words to solve the crossword.

Across

1. A small number.
3. Lots of moving vehicles.
5. The wind _____ all night.
6. A knife, fork and _____.
7. A room with a bath.
8. It is used to stick things together.
10. Got larger, taller or bigger.
12. To bite or munch food.
13. A child's picture magazine.
15. Expected at certain times.

Down

2. My dad goes to _____ at 7 am.
4. It is a help to solve a problem.
5. A witch flies on one.
6. I know I _____ always be good.
7. A room for sleeping in.
9. A colour that rhymes with 'clue'.
11. A packed meal eaten outdoors.
14. The workers on a ship.

Secret Code

4. Use the secret code to find the list word.

(a) ___ ___ ___
   (3) (2) (10)

(b) ___ ___ ___ ___
   (10) (7) (8) (5)

(c) ___ ___ ___ ___
   (1) (6) (9) (2)

(d) ___ ___ ___ ___
   (4) (8) (2) (10)

b	1
e	2
f	3
g	4
k	5
l	6
o	7
r	8
u	9
w	10

Word Challenge

5. Make as many words as you can from the letters in this word.

bathroom

ew | ue | oo | ic

List Words

blew
chew
grew
crew
few
glue
due
clue
blue
bathroom
bedroom
broomstick
spoon
traffic
comic
picnic
should
work

Revision Words

shoe
shut
short
fresh
brush
wish
two
three

Proofreading

6. Circle the incorrect words and rewrite them correctly in the spaces.

(a) You shoold clean your blew shoos for wurk.

_____

(b) Too of the crue are on a picknick.

_____

Missing Words

7. Complete the sentences using one of the list or revision words.

(a) My train is _____ at five o'clock.

(b) The plane and its _____ flew out an hour ago.

(c) Help your sister _____ her hair.

(d) The police directed the _____.

Shape Sorter

8. Write the word that fits in each shape.

(a)

(b)

(c)

Compound Words

9. Match the words to make compound words.

cut   room   stick

(a) bed_____

(b) broom_____

(c) bath_____

(d) short_____

Word Search

10. Find the list and revision words in the word search.

blew	due	broomstick
chew	clue	spoon
grew	blue	traffic
crew	bathroom	comic
few	bedroom	picnic
glue	work	should
shoe	shut	short
fresh	brush	wish
two	three	

t	s	h	o	e	l	n	v	g	g	l	u	e
w	d	t	b	r	o	o	m	s	t	i	c	k
o	u	r	r	g	r	e	w	v	r	t	l	g
i	e	a	u	s	h	u	t	h	r	e	e	l
r	s	f	s	p	i	c	n	i	c	e	s	j
g	p	f	h	c	l	u	e	j	l	q	w	c
s	o	i	t	m	z	y	d	b	l	u	e	o
h	o	c	n	b	o	b	e	d	r	o	o	m
o	n	w	o	r	k	s	h	o	u	l	d	i
r	b	a	t	h	r	o	o	m	w	o	c	c
t	p	t	v	u	f	r	e	s	h	a	h	a
v	c	r	e	w	g	c	x	l	z	f	e	w
q	n	z	w	i	s	h	c	b	l	e	w	q

Synonyms

11. Find list or revision words with similar meanings.

(a) funny _____

(b) closed _____

(c) job _____

(d) team _____

(e) chomp _____

(f) must _____

What am I?

12. (a) I am enjoyable.
I am packaged in a bag.
I include food and drink.
You usually eat me outdoors.

I am a [＿＿＿＿＿＿]

(b) I come in different colours.
I come in pairs.
I have a sole.

I am a [＿＿＿＿＿＿]

Additional Activities

13. (a) Write six more 'colour' words. Check your spelling.

(b) Write your new colour words in alphabetical order.

(c) For each colour word, write a list of four objects that are usually this colour.

Unit 2

o saying u | **-ck**

 Look

 Say

 Trace

 Cover

 Write

Check

List Words	Practise	Practise	T	D
love				
above				
oven				
cover				
mother				
brother				
another				
other				
Monday				
front				
onion				
back				
trick				
brick				
shock				
luck				
Ireland				
March				

Antonyms

Antonyms are words with the opposite meaning. 'Hot' and 'cold' are antonyms.

1. Find a list word with the opposite meaning.

   (a) father _____

   (b) below _____

   (c) hate _____

   (d) sister _____

Word Maker

2. Join 'ck' to the end of the letters in the circles to make new words.

 sho

tri **ck**

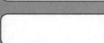 bri

o saying u | -ck

Crossword

3. Use list words to solve the crossword.

Across
2. One more.
4. A vegetable.
5. Opposite of front.
7. To adore.
9. Third month of the year.
11. I saw him the _____ day.
12. A country beginning with 'I'.
14. It is used in building.
15. Opposite of father.
16. Over.

Down
1. You cook in this.
3. I can do a good card _____.
6. A lid, top or cap.
8. She touched the wire and got a _____.
9. Day before Tuesday.
10. Opposite of back.
13. We wished him _____ in his test.
14. Opposite of sister.

Syllables

4. Add the missing syllable to finish the list word.

(a) o + ther >>> [   ]

(b) a + [   ] >>> [   ]

(c) Ire + [   ] >>> [   ]

(d) mo + [   ] >>> [   ]

(e) Mon + [   ] >>> [   ]

Word Worm

5. Circle each list word you can find in the word worm.

ovenluckonionanothercoverMarchbrickfront

o saying u **-ck**

List Words

- love
- above
- oven
- cover
- mother
- brother
- another
- other
- Monday
- front
- onion
- back
- trick
- brick
- shock
- luck
- Ireland
- March

Revision Words

- such
- chin
- chip
- lunch
- punch
- church
- four
- five

Word Hunt

6. (a) Which list words have the same five letters?

(b) Which list words start with a capital letter?

(c) Which list word is in the word 'glove'?

Plurals

7. Add 's' or 'es' to make these words plural.

(a) mother [ ]   (b) church [ ]

(c) lunch [ ]   (d) shock [ ]

(e) onion [ ]   (f) trick [ ]

Alphabetical Order

8. Write these list and revision words in alphabetical order.

Ireland   back
punch   oven
          cover

_____

_____

_____

_____

_____

Word Search

9. Find the list and revision words in the word search.

love	another	trick
above	other	brick
oven	Monday	shock
cover	front	luck
mother	onion	Ireland
brother	back	March
such	chin	chip
lunch	punch	church
four	five	

u	l	a	o	n	i	o	n	l	u	c	k	a
e	u	o	f	t	x	l	s	h	o	c	k	g
a	n	t	g	o	l	o	y	f	r	o	n	t
b	c	h	c	M	r	v	u	i	c	h	i	p
o	h	e	h	o	e	e	j	t	r	i	c	k
v	n	r	u	n	l	b	s	c	o	v	e	r
e	w	c	r	d	a	r	k	p	u	n	c	h
b	b	c	c	a	n	o	t	h	e	r	y	d
b	r	h	h	y	d	t	s	u	c	h	j	a
a	i	i	e	r	y	h	i	f	i	v	e	o
c	c	n	j	m	i	e	m	o	t	h	e	r
k	k	m	f	o	u	r	a	l	t	x	t	d
b	g	w	M	a	r	c	h	y	o	v	e	n

All Mixed Up

10. Unjumble these list and revision words.

(a) cshu _____   (b) cbirk _____

(c) nooni _____   (d) hroatne _____

(e) rfuo _____   (f) rotherb _____

Magic Words

11. Change the first word into the last word by changing one letter on each line to make a new word.

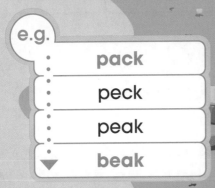

e.g.
| pack |
| peck |
| peak |
| beak |

(a)
| love |
| |
| |
| post |

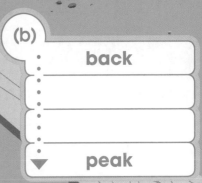

(b)
| back |
| |
| |
| peak |

Additional Activities

12. (a) Write five more words that end in '**ck**'. Check your spelling.

(b) Use a dictionary to write a definition for each of your new '**ck**' words.

(c) Write five sentences, each containing one of your new '**ck**' words.

Unit 3

Look

Say

Trace

Cover

Write

Check

List Words	Practise	Practise	T	D
think				
thank				
sunk				
plank				
fine				
alive				
line				
reply				
supply				
apply				
fried				
tried				
cried				
high				
sigh				
right				
while				
which				

Missing Vowels

1. Write a, e, i or u to make list words.

   (a) fr ___ ___ d

   (b) ___ pply

   (c) s ___ nk

   (d) wh ___ l ___

   (e) s ___ gh

   (f) l ___ n ___

Synonyms

2. Find a list word with a similar meaning.

   (a) answer _____

   (b) board _____

   (c) living _____

   (d) correct _____

   (e) provide _____

Crossword

3. Use list words to solve the crossword.

Across

1. To believe or imagine.
4. Opposite of wrong.
5. _____ one do you prefer?
8. Feeling well.
9. Answer.
10. Opposite of dead.
12. Made an effort to do something.
14. Long flat piece of wood.
16. To provide.

2. Opposite of low.
3. He let out a _____ when the exam was over.
5. During.
6. Shed tears.
7. Cooked in hot oil.
11. I tried to write along the _____.
12. _____ you for coming to my party.
13. To put to use.
15. The pirate ship was _____.

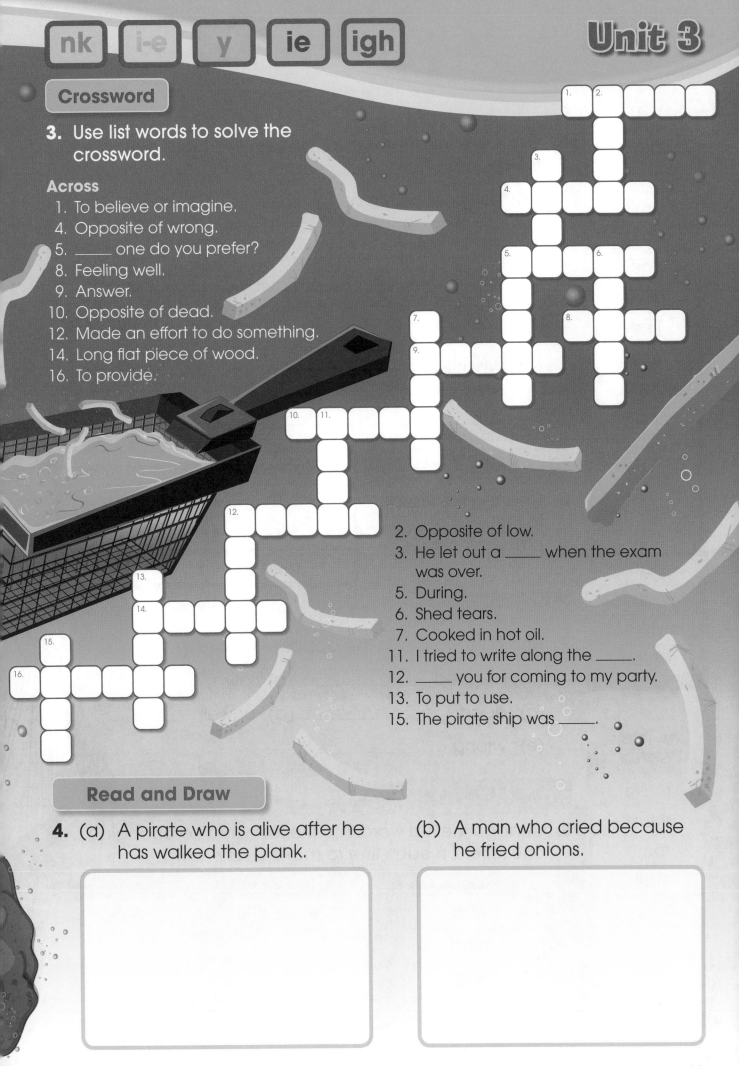

Read and Draw

4. (a) A pirate who is alive after he has walked the plank.

(b) A man who cried because he fried onions.

nk i-e y ie igh

List Words

think
thank
sunk
plank
fine
alive
line
reply
supply
apply
fried
tried
cried
high
sigh
right
while
which

Proofreading

5. Circle the incorrect words and rewrite them correctly in the spaces.

(a) He gave a sy as he tryed but failed to score a goal.

[_____] [_____]

(b) I'll be fin whaisle you are away.

[_____] [_____]

(c) Witch is the write path?

[_____] [_____]

Changing the Tense

6. Change the words to the past or present tense.

Past tense	Present tense
	supply
cried	
fried	

Antonyms

7. Find a list word with the opposite meaning.

(a) laughed _____   (b) low _____

(c) dead _____   (d) unwell _____

(e) wrong _____

Magic Words

8. Change the first word into the last word by changing one letter on each line to make a new word.

e.g.
bird
bind
find
fine

(a)
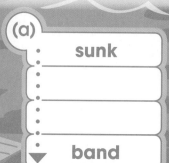
sunk

band

(b)

fine

lame

Revision Words

these
them
tooth
bath
it's
I'll
only
one

My Spelling Workbook C—Prim-Ed Publishing—www.prim-ed.com

Word Search

9. Find the list and revision words in the word search.

think	line	cried
thank	reply	high
sunk	supply	sigh
plank	apply	right
fine	fried	while
alive	tried	which
these	them	tooth
bath	it's	I'll
only	one	

e	g	o	u	w	h	i	c	h	y	e	x	i
t	x	n	a	s	u	p	p	l	y	t	i	i
h	c	e	l	w	v	h	i	g	h	h	l	j
a	r	i	i	n	w	w	h	i	l	e	l	p
n	i	a	v	r	r	e	p	l	y	s	b	l
k	e	p	e	i	i	t	s	z	t	e	m	a
p	d	p	c	g	h	l	z	k	r	f	a	n
u	k	l	x	h	o	n	l	y	i	r	t	k
x	m	y	d	t	h	i	n	k	e	i	b	r
m	t	o	o	t	h	y	b	o	d	e	a	e
t	h	e	m	f	i	n	e	z	s	d	t	a
e	s	u	n	k	v	z	t	s	i	g	h	m
t	e	g	b	m	l	i	n	e	y	z	p	k

Rhyming Words

10. Choose a rhyming word from your list or revision words.

(a) path _____

(b) five _____

(c) rich _____

(d) sink _____

(e) please _____

(f) night _____

Secret Code

11. Use the secret code to find the list or revision word.

(a) ___ ___ ___ ___
   (2) (1) (10) (4)

(b) ___ ___ ___ ___ ___
   (1) (7) (5) (11) (3)

(c) ___ ___ ___ ___ ___
   (1) (9) (9) (7) (12)

(d) ___ ___ ___ ___ ___
   (9) (7) (1) (8) (6)

a	1
b	2
e	3
h	4
i	5
k	6
l	7
n	8
p	9
t	10
v	11
y	12

Additional Activities

12. (a) Write five more words that end in '**nk**'.

(b) Write your new words in alphabetical order.

(c) Write five sentences, each containing one of your new '**nk**' words.

Unit 4

ll	**ss**	**zz**	**ff**

Look

Say

Trace

Cover

Write

Check

List Words	Practise	Practise	T	D
still				
smell				
skull				
stall				
across				
dress				
glass				
miss				
jazz				
buzz				
fizz				
dizzy				
cuff				
staff				
cliff				
stuff				
yesterday				
April				

Small Words

1. Find smaller words in these words.

(a) stall _____

_____

(b) miss _____

(c) still _____

(d) cliff _____

(e) smell _____

Antonyms

2. Find a list word with the opposite meaning.

(a) today _____

(b) hit _____

(c) moving _____

(d) strip _____

Crossword

3. Use list words to solve the crossword.

Across

3. Not moving.
5. The end part of your sleeve.
7. Feeling of your head spinning.
8. A type of music.
11. The day before today.
15. A scent or odour.
16. Fail to hit or reach something.
17. A stand for the sale of goods.
18. Things, objects or articles.

Down

1. A spring month.
2. The workers.
4. To make a humming noise.
6. Bubbles of gas in a liquid.
9. From one side to another.
10. To put on clothes.
12. The bones around a head.
13. A steep rock face.
14. Windows are mostly made of _____.

Synonyms

4. Find a list word with a similar meaning.

(a) wobbly _____

(b) bubble _____

(c) hum _____

(d) stink _____

(e) things _____

Word Challenge

5. Make as many words as you can from the letters in this word.

yesterday

Unit 4

ll **ss** **zz** **ff**

BzZZ z zz ZZZ

List Words

- still
- smell
- skull
- stall
- across
- dress
- glass
- miss
- jazz
- buzz
- fizz
- dizzy
- cuff
- staff
- cliff
- stuff
- yesterday
- April

Revision Words

- around
- house
- now
- down
- why
- where
- May
- many

Homographs

The word '**dress**' is a homograph. This means that it has two meanings. One meaning is a verb – a doing word; the second is a noun – a naming word.

6. Write one sentence using '**dress**' as a verb and one using it as a noun.

(a) _____

(b) _____

Guess the Word

7. Write list words to match the clues.

(a) Bees do this. _____

(b) Protects your brain. _____

(c) Rhymes with '**will**'. _____

(d) Girls wear this. _____

Word Hunt

8. (a) Which list or revision words have the letter '**m**'?

(b) Which revision word rhymes with '**mouse**'?

(c) Which list words begin with '**st**'?

Unit 4

ll ss zz ff

Word Search

9. Find the list and revision words in the word search.

still	glass	cuff
smell	miss	staff
skull	jazz	cliff
stall	buzz	stuff
across	fizz	yesterday
dress	dizzy	April
around	house	now
down	why	where
May	many	

w	h	y	s	t	i	l	l	y	h	d	m	l
s	l	s	d	w	g	A	g	e	n	m	e	j
t	l	c	v	g	c	p	r	s	t	a	l	l
u	d	i	z	z	y	r	s	t	a	f	f	c
f	d	o	w	n	h	i	k	e	b	l	n	d
f	b	u	z	z	o	l	q	r	i	x	x	r
k	m	a	n	y	u	f	d	d	p	v	a	e
a	c	r	o	s	s	g	l	a	s	s	r	s
j	s	p	w	h	e	r	e	y	q	f	o	s
a	k	p	M	a	y	c	u	f	f	i	u	p
z	u	s	a	k	u	p	o	k	b	z	n	v
z	l	s	m	e	l	l	x	z	m	z	d	u
c	l	i	f	f	e	n	o	w	m	i	s	s

Missing Letters

10. Complete these list and revision words.

(a) di ___ z ___   (b) w ___ e ___ e

(c) ___ li ___ f   (d) g ___ ___ ___ ss

Spelling Sums

11. Find list or revision words.

(a) **yes + ter + day** = _____   (b) **c + uff** = _____

(c) **Ap + ril** = _____   (d) **M + ay** = _____

(e) **st + all** = _____   (f) **j + azz** = _____

Changing Words

12. Change one letter in each word to make a list or revision word.

(a) grass _____

(b) kiss _____

(c) not _____

(d) skill _____

Additional Activities

13. (a) Write five more words that end in '**ss**'. Check your spelling.

(b) Use a dictionary to write a definition for each of your new words.

(c) Write five sentences, each containing one of your new '**ss**' words.

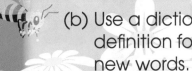

Unit 5

le

 Look
 Say
 Trace
 Cover
 Write
 Check

List Words	Practise	Practise	T	D
bottle				
little				
battle				
rattle				
middle				
riddle				
paddle				
buckle				
ankle				
eagle				
apple				
needle				
able				
rectangle				
single				
jungle				
part				
twelve				

Picture Matching

1. Write the list word that matches each picture.

(a) _____

(b) _____

(c) _____

(d) _____

What am I?

2. (a) I am an even number.

I am twice six.

I am less than thirteen.

I am _____.

(b) I can be hard to understand.

I can be fun.

I make you think.

I am a _____.

Crossword

3. Use list words to solve the crossword.

Across

1. A fight or struggle.
4. Something that is hard to understand.
5. You use one to travel in a canoe.
7. To bang, clatter or jangle.
9. A bit or piece.
11. Small.
13. I am _____ to go to the party.
14. It can contain liquid or sauce.
15. A round fruit with red or green skin.
17. The _____ is full of wild animals.
18. You use it for sewing or knitting.

Down

2. It connects a foot to a leg.
3. Central.
6. Only one.
8. A dozen.
10. A shape.
12. A large bird of prey.
16. It's on the end of a belt or strap.

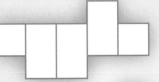

Shape Sorter

4. Write a list word that fits in each shape.

(a)

(b)

(c)

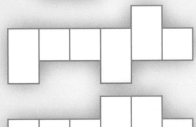

Letters into Words

5. Write five list words using the letters on the hearts.

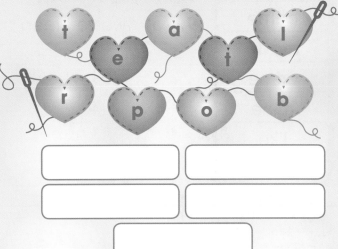

t e a i t r p o b

List Words

bottle
little
battle
rattle
middle
riddle
paddle
buckle
ankle
eagle
apple
needle
able
rectangle
single
jungle
part
twelve

Adding Endings

These words are nouns (naming words). To make them into verbs (doing words), we add 'ing'. When 'ing' is added, 'e' goes away.

6. Add 'ing' to each of these words.

(a) paddle _____

(b) rattle _____

(c) battle _____

(d) buckle _____

Missing Words

7. Complete the sentences using list or revision words.

(a) Dad's belt has a silver _____.

(b) The _____ lion cub was sad because he was lost in the _____ of the _____.

(c) I _____ to _____ cakes.

All Mixed Up

8. Unjumble these list and revision words.

(a) mdledi _____

(b) mreci _____

(c) tabtel _____

(d) velwet _____

Read and Draw

9. (a) Twelve green bottles

(b) A single red apple

Revision Words

make
came
made
crime
mine
like
her
come

Word Search

10. Find the list and revision words in the word search.

bottle   paddle   able

little   buckle   rectangle

battle   ankle   single

rattle   eagle   jungle

middle   apple   part

riddle   needle   twelve

make   came   made

crime   mine   like

her   come

x	x	m	a	z	t	o	c	m	a	k	e	m
a	k	q	i	v	w	e	r	b	b	t	n	w
m	i	d	d	l	e	r	i	u	a	y	s	p
x	j	u	n	g	l	e	m	c	t	w	i	a
u	h	o	y	l	v	c	e	k	t	b	n	r
n	e	e	d	l	e	t	a	l	l	o	g	t
r	r	s	m	r	l	a	l	e	e	t	l	y
i	c	q	a	a	i	n	i	c	x	t	e	b
d	o	a	d	t	k	g	t	a	d	l	a	a
d	m	b	e	t	e	l	t	m	l	e	g	n
l	e	l	c	l	f	e	l	e	a	n	l	k
e	o	e	t	e	t	l	e	m	i	n	e	l
p	a	d	d	l	e	z	w	a	p	p	l	e

Rhyming Words

11. Choose a rhyming word from your list or revision words.

(a) tingle _____

(b) start _____

(c) same _____

(d) saddle _____

(e) table _____

(f) spike _____

Word Worm

12. Circle each list or revision word you can find in the word worm.

likeneedlebottlemaketwelvebuckle

Additional Activities

13. (a) Write four more 'shape' words. Check your spelling.

(b) Write your new shape words in alphabetical order.

(c) For each shape word, write a list of three objects that are usually this shape.

Unit 6

scr spr str

Look

Say

Trace

Cover

Write

Check

List Words	Practise	Practise	T	D
scrap				
scrape				
scrub				
scream				
screen				
spray				
spread				
sprain				
sprint				
sprout				
stripe				
strap				
straw				
street				
strong				
stream				
live				
usual				

Adding Beginnings

1. Add 'scr', 'str', or 'spr' to make a list word.

(a) _ _ _ ub

(b) _ _ _ ay

(c) _ _ _ ong

(d) _ _ _ ap

(e) _ _ _ ape

(f) _ _ _ ain

Small Words

2. Write the list words that contain these small words.

(a) us _____

(b) out _____

(c) ape _____

(d) raw _____

(e) tree _____

(f) on _____

My Spelling Workbook C—Prim-Ed Publishing—www.prim-ed.com

Crossword

3. Use list words to solve the crossword.

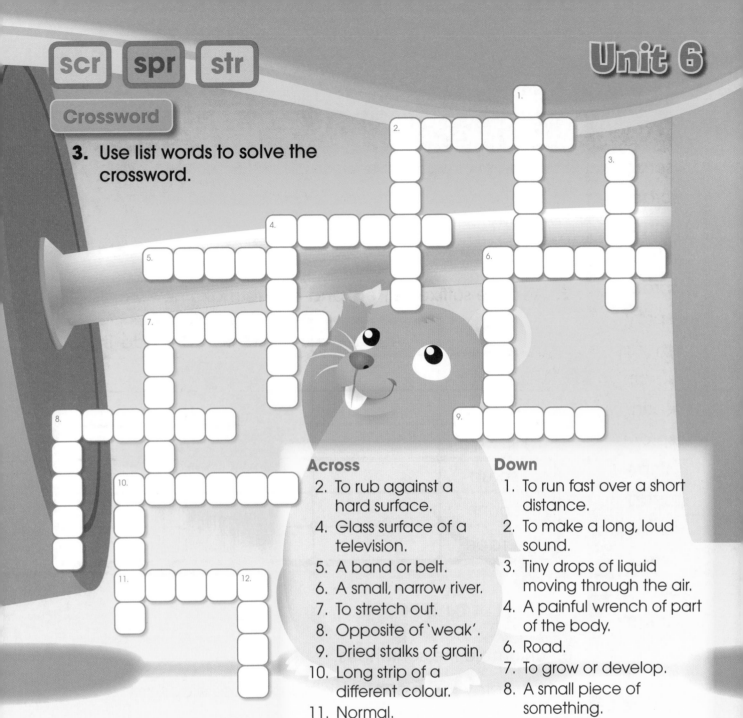

Across

2. To rub against a hard surface.
4. Glass surface of a television.
5. A band or belt.
6. A small, narrow river.
7. To stretch out.
8. Opposite of 'weak'.
9. Dried stalks of grain.
10. Long strip of a different colour.
11. Normal.

Down

1. To run fast over a short distance.
2. To make a long, loud sound.
3. Tiny drops of liquid moving through the air.
4. A painful wrench of part of the body.
6. Road.
7. To grow or develop.
8. A small piece of something.
10. Rub hard so as to clean.
12. He went to _____ in America.

Spelling Patterns

4. Use the correct colour for these words.

(a) Colour the '**scr**' words **red**.

(b) Colour the '**spr**' words **blue**.

(c) Colour the '**str**' words **green**.

scream	sprout
spray	street
strong	scrap

List Words

scrap
scrape
scrub
scream
screen
spray
spread
sprain
sprint
sprout
stripe
strap
straw
street
strong
stream
live
usual

Adding Endings

1. For some words, the endings are just added.

2. For some words, the consonant is doubled to keep the vowel short.

3. 'e' goes away when 'ing' comes to stay.

5. Add the suffixes 's', 'ed' and 'ing' to make new words.

	Add 's'	Add 'ed'	Add 'ing'
(a) live			
(b) use			
(c) spray			
(d) scrub			
(e) sprint			
(f) scrape			

Mixed-up Sentences

6. Unjumble the sentences.

(a) spray to An can trunk its water. use elephant

_____

(b) scrub could your hard. scrape hand if you You too

_____

Revision Words

woke
bone
note
June
cube
use
seven
eight

Proofreading

7. Circle the incorrect words and rewrite them correctly in the spaces.

(a) You can see ate fish in the steam.

[_____] [_____]

(b) My name and streat were written on the nowt.

[_____] [_____]

Word Search

8. Find the list and revision words in the word search.

scrap	spread	straw
scrape	sprain	street
scrub	sprint	strong
scream	sprout	stream
screen	stripe	live
spray	strap	usual
woke	bone	note
June	cube	use
seven	eight	

l	w	J	c	y	s	c	r	a	p	u	s	e
i	o	u	u	s	p	r	e	a	d	n	p	n
v	k	n	b	s	t	r	e	a	m	o	r	b
e	e	e	e	t	s	p	r	o	u	t	a	f
f	p	s	c	r	e	e	n	y	p	e	y	s
s	s	p	r	i	n	t	u	s	u	a	l	p
c	n	s	x	p	u	s	t	r	a	w	b	r
r	b	t	s	e	m	b	t	k	o	l	d	a
u	f	r	c	x	s	s	t	r	o	n	g	i
b	y	a	r	r	e	a	q	a	m	w	w	n
a	e	p	e	r	v	e	u	e	i	g	h	t
s	c	r	a	p	e	x	b	o	n	e	n	s
r	h	y	m	a	n	s	t	r	e	e	t	x

Secret Words

9. (a) Take 'st' off 'stream' and put in 'c'. _____

(b) Put 'un' in front of 'usual'. _____

(c) Add 'een' to the end of 'eight'. _____

(d) Take 'p' off 'scrap' and put in 'tch'. _____

Word Meanings

10. Draw lines to match the words to their meanings.

(a) sprain •——————• normal

(b) sprint •——————• monitor

(c) screen •——————• twist

(d) usual •——————• dash

Additional Activities

11. (a) Write five more words that start with 'str'. Check your spelling.

(b) Use a dictionary to write a definition for each of your new 'str' words.

(c) Write five sentences each containing one of your new 'str' words.

Unit 7

Look

Say

Trace

Cover

Write

Check

List Words	Practise	Practise	T	D
cracker				
lights				
birth				
stocking				
snowflakes				
Advent				
Dasher				
December				
balloon				
greetings				
holiday				
donkey				
Jesus				
Christmas				
Donner				
shopping				
minute				
month				

Letters into Words

1. Write three list words using the letters on the stars. (Letters can be used more than once.)

   _____

   _____

   _____

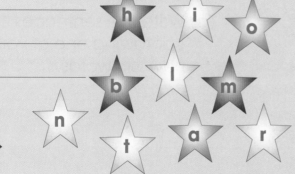

Missing Letters

2. Complete these list words.

   (a) m __ n __ __ __ e

   (b) __ __ v __ __ t

   (c) __ __ __ k __ __

   (d) h __ __ __ __ d __ __

   (e) __ __ gh __ __

Christmas

Crossword

3. Use list words to solve the crossword.

Across

2. Name of a reindeer who is probably fast.
7. Expression of goodwill.
9. There are 60 of these in an hour.
10. There are 12 of these in a year.
12. The son of God.
15. Blow it up.
16. Pull hard!
17. The _____ calendar was full of sweets.
18. We went on _____ to France.

Down

1. Twelfth month of the year.
3. You only see these when it's cold.
4. On Saturday we went _____ for presents.
5. The Christian festival celebrating Christ's birth.
6. Christmas tree decorations.
8. Mary rode on one.
11. Another of Santa's reindeers.
13. You hope it will be filled.
14. Being born.

Secret Code

a	b	c	d	e	g	h	i	m	n	o	r	s	t	u	x	y	z
1	2	3	4	5	6	7	8	9	10	11	12	13	14	15	16	17	18

4. Use the secret code to find the Christmas message.

___ ___ ___ ___ ___ ___ ___ ___ ___   ___ ___ ___ ___ ___ ___ ___ ___ ___   ___ ___   ___ ___ ___
(3) (7) (12) (8) (13)(14) (9) (1) (13)   (6) (12) (5) (5) (14) (8) (10) (6) (13)   (14)(11)   (17)(11)(15)

Unit 7

List Words

- cracker
- lights
- birth
- stocking
- snowflakes
- Advent
- Dasher
- December
- balloon
- greetings
- holiday
- donkey
- Jesus
- Christmas
- Donner
- shopping
- minute
- month

Revision Words

- tinsel
- carrot
- Santa
- carol
- sweets
- sing
- any
- more

Proofreading

5. Circle the incorrect words and rewrite them correctly in the spaces.

(a) Can I shing my favourite karl at the Crismas concert?

（　　　　　）（　　　　　）（　　　　　）

(b) Emma fed the doncay a carot.

（　　　　　）（　　　　　）

Missing Words

6. Complete the sentences using one of the list or revision words.

(a) _____ and _____ pull _____'s sleigh.

(b) I hang a _____ on my bed at _____.

(c) Do not blow _____ air into that _____.

(d) We get presents in the _____ of _____.

Word Shapes

7. Write the word that fits in each shape.

(a)

(b)

(c)

(d)

Christmas

Word Search

8. Find the list and revision words in the Christmas tree word search.

cracker   lights
birth   stocking
snowflakes   Advent
Dasher   December
balloon   greetings
holiday   donkey
Jesus   Christmas
Donner   shopping
minute   month
tinsel   carrot
Santa   carol
sweets   sing
any   more

Word search grid (Christmas tree shape):

```
            D
          h a v
        k e s s g
      l i g h t s n
        A e o
      d d r c s
    D o v b k w s
  m o n e a i e n o
q o n k n l n e o x s
  n e t l g t w
  t e y x o b s f h
  c a r o l o b r l o m
s h o p p i n g t a l i c
g r e e t i n g s a k i n g j
  J c r a c k e r e d u
  D e c e m b e r o s a t y
p n s S a n t a m k r y e t m
x t j u t i n s e l r z a n y l u
C h r i s t m a s v b b k c a r r o t
    m o r e i
    s i n g r
    u c q c t
    m o n t h
```

Read and Draw

9. Santa is putting gifts under the tree.

What am I?

10. We only last a short time.
We are very, very light.
We sparkle.
We are cold.

We are _____.

Additional Activities

11. (a) Write six more Christmas words. Check your spelling.

(b) Write a Christmas message to your friends.

(c) Write your Christmas list to Santa.

Unit 8

Look

Say

Trace

Cover

Write

Check

List Words	Practise	Practise	T	D
quit				
quiet				
quite				
liquid				
queen				
question				
quack				
quilt				
quake				
squad				
squash				
squeak				
squirt				
squeal				
squirm				
square				
oil				
during				

qu squ

Rhyming Words

Small Words

1. Choose a rhyming word from the list words.

(a) knit _____

(b) boil _____

(c) meal _____

(d) speak _____

(e) spare _____

(f) stack _____

2. Find smaller words in these words.

(a) quite _____ _____

(b) square _____

(c) during _____

_____

(d) question _____

_____ _____

My Spelling Workbook C—Prim-Ed Publishing—www.prim-ed.com

qu | squ

Crossword

3. Use list words to solve the crossword.

Across

2. I heard a cat _____ the night.
5. To make a high-pitched scream.
8. To wriggle or twist.
9. A shape with four equal sides.
11. A small number of soldiers.
13. Little or no noise.
15. To shake, especially the earth.
16. A thick cover for a bed.

Down

1. Ask one when you want an answer.
3. To crush until flat.
4. A short high-pitched sound.
6. Water is a _____.
7. Shoot water out from a small hole.
10. My teacher always says '_____ right'.
12. The sound made by a duck.
14. Thick greasy liquid.
15. Opposite of king.
16. To leave or stop.

Word Worm

4. Circle each list word you can find in the word worm.

quietsquarequeensquashoilsqueak

What am I?

5. Write a list word to match each clue.

(a) I have four equal sides. _____

(b) I am a female ruler. _____

(c) I am a thick greasy liquid. _____

(d) I am a bed cover. _____

(e) I am a team of people. _____

(f) I am a drink made with juice. _____

`qu` `squ`

List Words

quit
quiet
quite
liquid
queen
question
quack
quilt
quake
squad
squash
squeak
squirt
squeal
squirm
square
oil
during

Revision Words

drop
grab
try
trim
brave
crash
back
give

Missing Words

6. Complete the sentences using the list or revision words.

(a) _____ the night I heard a mouse _____.

(b) _____ some _____ on the wheel.

(c) I always _____ to answer the _____.

Secret Words

7. (a) Take 'qu' off 'quick' and put in 'br'. _____

(b) Take 'squ' off 'squeal' and put in 'm'. _____

(c) Take 'a' out of 'quack' and put in 'i'. _____

(d) Add 'ly' to the end of 'quiet'. _____

(e) Take 'cr' off 'crash' and put in 'spl'. _____

Letters into Words

8. Write six list or revision words using the letters on the shells.

q s o

l e i

u a t

Squeak Squeak

Change the Tense

9. Change the words to past tense.

(a) crash _____   (b) question _____

(c) quack _____   (d) squash _____

(e) squirt _____   (f) squeak _____

Word Search

10. Find the list and revision words in the word search.

quit	quack	squirt
quiet	quake	squeal
quite	quilt	squirm
liquid	squad	square
queen	squash	oil
question	squeak	during
drop	grab	try
trim	brave	crash
back	give	

q	z	b	r	a	v	e	s	g	s	d	w	f
q	s	q	u	a	d	x	l	i	q	u	i	d
f	s	q	u	a	k	e	b	v	u	r	j	r
b	s	q	u	e	a	l	w	e	i	i	o	o
s	q	u	e	a	k	r	q	y	r	n	k	p
o	i	l	q	u	i	t	u	w	t	g	c	b
q	u	a	c	k	q	x	e	z	j	s	r	x
u	c	r	s	q	u	a	s	h	e	q	a	t
i	q	g	a	y	d	q	t	g	e	u	s	r
t	e	u	t	s	q	u	i	r	m	a	h	y
e	t	r	i	m	k	i	o	x	g	r	a	b
h	q	u	e	e	n	e	n	s	z	e	o	j
c	d	b	a	c	k	t	q	u	i	l	t	z

Antonyms

11. Find list or revision words with the opposite meaning.

(a) take _____   (b) king _____

(c) noisy _____   (d) answer _____

(e) solid _____   (f) front _____

Spelling Patterns

12. Use the correct colour for these words.

(a) Colour the 'qu' words orange.

(b) Colour the 'squ' words green.

(c) Colour all other words blue.

squad

quake

queen

during

brave

squirm

Additional Activities

13. (a) Write five more 'qu' words. Check your spelling.

(b) Use a dictionary to write a definition for each of your new 'qu' words.

(c) Write five sentences, each containing one of your new 'qu' words.

Unit 9

old ind

 Look
 Say
 Trace
 Cover
 Write
 Check

List Words	Practise	Practise	T	D
told				
older				
folder				
golden				
scold				
coldest				
boldest				
goldfish				
kindest				
remind				
behind				
find				
mind				
wind				
blind				
grind				
again				
name				

Shape Sorter

1. Write the word that fits in each shape.

(a)

(b)

(c)

(d)

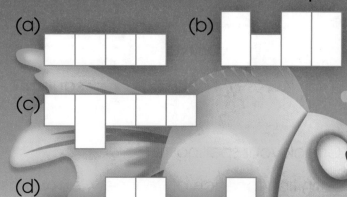

Changing Words

2. Change one letter in each word to make a list word.

(a) wand _____

(b) mine _____

(c) colder _____

(d) sold _____

(e) fond _____

(f) blend _____

old ind

Crossword

3. Use list words to solve the crossword.

Across

1. At the back.
2. Turn a handle to make something work.
4. A pet that swims in a bowl.
6. The most caring.
9. I keep all my papers in a ____.
11. Today was the ____ day of the year.
15. By what someone is known.
16. Coloured like a yellow metal.

Down

1. Put a 'b' in front of oldest.
3. Unable to see.
5. I forgot the answer as my ____ went blank.
7. Past tense of 'tell'.
8. To cause one to remember.
10. Once more.
12. She is six years ____ than I.
13. The teacher had to ____ the naughty boys.
14. To crush coffee beans.

Alphabetical Order

4. Write these words in alphabetical order.

mind	told	name
again		older

_____

_____

_____

_____

Word Hunt

5. Which list word …

(a) can be pronounced in two different ways?

_____

(b) contains another list word?

_____

(c) has the most letters? _____

(d) starts with 'a'? _____

Unit 9

List Words

- told
- older
- folder
- golden
- scold
- coldest
- boldest
- goldfish
- kindest
- remind
- behind
- find
- mind
- wind
- blind
- grind
- again
- name

Revision Words

- start
- stone
- stamp
- nest
- must
- lost
- nine
- help

Comparatives

The suffix 'er' means 'more' and the suffix 'est' means 'most'; for example, tall, taller, tallest.

6. Complete this grid.

Word	'er'	'est'
	older	
cold		
bold		

Secret Code

7. Use the secret code to find the list or revision word.

(a) __ __ __ __ __ __
   (1) (3) (4) (5) (8) (2)

(b) __ __ __ __
   (8) (5) (8) (3)

(c) __ __ __ __
   (7) (5) (8) (2)

(d) __ __ __ __
   (10) (9) (6) (2)

b	1
d	2
e	3
h	4
i	5
l	6
m	7
n	8
o	9
t	10

Read and Draw

8. (a) A goldfish hiding behind a stone

(b) A nest containing a golden egg

Word Search

9. Find the list and revision words in the word search.

told	older	folder
golden	scold	coldest
boldest	goldfish	kindest
remind	behind	find
mind	wind	blind
grind	again	name
start	stone	stamp
nest	must	lost
nine	help	

b	l	i	n	d	d	y	m	b	a	n	j	k
g	r	i	n	d	r	b	u	o	n	s	a	z
t	a	d	u	v	e	j	s	l	s	t	y	n
o	g	s	u	h	m	f	t	d	g	a	h	a
l	a	c	f	u	i	o	b	e	o	r	e	m
d	i	o	g	k	n	l	e	s	l	t	l	e
s	n	l	o	i	d	d	h	t	d	p	p	o
f	i	d	l	n	l	e	i	m	f	a	x	l
j	n	e	d	d	o	r	n	i	i	s	f	d
w	e	s	e	e	s	v	d	n	s	t	x	e
i	t	t	n	s	t	n	c	d	h	o	v	r
n	n	e	s	t	a	m	p	f	i	n	d	i
d	y	n	s	c	o	l	d	d	p	e	r	h

Past Tense

When something has already happened, we often add 'ed' to the word. Some words change altogether:

'**start**' becomes '**started**'

'**bind**' becomes '**bound**'

10. Change these words to the past tense.

(a) find _____

(b) grind _____

(c) help _____

(d) name _____

Word Worm

11. Circle each list or revision word you can find in the word worm.

Additional Activities

12. (a) Write two adjectives that end in '**old**' and two that end in '**ind**'. Check your spelling.

(b) Add '**er**' to the end of your four new words. Do they make sense?

(c) Add '**est**' to the end of you four new words. Do they make sense?

Unit 10

Look

Say

Trace

Cover

Write

Check

List Words	Practise	Practise	T	D
twice				
price				
spice				
slice				
ice-cream				
rice				
advice				
mice				
voice				
ace				
disgrace				
trace				
space				
place				
race				
face				
January				
because				

Word Building

1. Use the letters in the ice–cream to make 'ice' words.

_____

_____

_____

_____

_____

-cream

sp

pr

tw

sl

More Word Building

2. Use the letters in the face to make 'ace' words.

_____

_____

_____

_____

_____

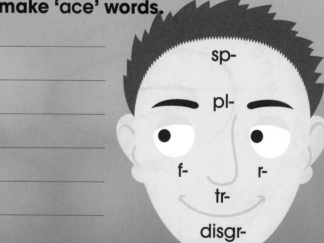

sp-

pl-

f-

r-

tr-

disgrice ace

Crossword

3. Use list words to solve the crossword.

Across

2. A playing card with a single symbol.
5. A competition between runners.
7. Two times.
9. A particular position.
12. Cereal grains.
13. Gap.
14. You add this to flavour food.
15. Ideas, help, hints.
17. His bad behaviour was a ____.

Down

1. Mark, sign or evidence.
3. The 1st month.
4. Plural of mouse.
6. He left work ____ he was ill.
8. Soft, frozen, milky dessert.
9. Cost.
10. The part of your head where your nose and eyes are.
11. A piece, portion or wedge.
16. The power of speech.

Word Challenge

4. Make four compound words using the word 'space'.

ship
suit   boat
space
craft   man
port   light

Syllables

5. Add the missing syllable to finish the list word.

(a) ice + cream ▶▶▶ _____

(b) dis + [   ] ▶▶▶ _____

(c) be + [   ] ▶▶▶ _____

(d) ad + [   ] ▶▶▶ _____

Unit 10

List Words

- twice
- price
- spice
- slice
- ice-cream
- rice
- advice
- mice
- voice
- ace
- disgrace
- trace
- space
- place
- race
- face
- January
- because

Revision Words

- skip
- skirt
- spark
- spot
- swim
- sweep
- good
- who

Mixed-up Sentences

6. Unjumble the sentences.

(a) have I ice-cream? a of cake and slice some May

_____

(b) are best sales. prices in The the January

_____

All Mixed Up

7. Unjumble these list and revision words.

(a) wicet _____

(b) cripe _____

(c) ebaecus _____

(d) cafe _____

(e) tops _____

(f) how _____

Secret Words

8. (a) Take 'use' off 'because' and put in 'me'. _____

(b) Take 'grace' off 'disgrace' and put in 'may'. _____

(c) Take 'k' off 'spark' and put in 'e'. _____

Read and Draw

9. (a) Three mice in a skipping race

(b) A sad face with a spot on its chin

Word Search

10. Find the list and revision words in the word search.

twice	advice	space
price	mice	place
spice	voice	race
slice	ace	face
ice-cream	disgrace	January
rice	trace	because
skip	skirt	spark
spot	swim	sweep
good	who	

y	e	p	r	i	c	e	k	b	p	q	b	i
y	s	a	p	d	i	s	g	r	a	c	e	c
s	l	w	c	s	p	a	r	k	s	m	c	e
k	i	u	t	r	i	q	i	e	k	z	a	c
i	c	z	w	f	f	s	c	t	i	n	u	r
p	e	g	i	r	a	c	e	r	r	g	s	e
s	p	a	c	e	w	l	g	a	t	p	e	a
u	s	w	e	e	p	m	i	c	e	l	j	m
s	g	s	w	i	m	a	c	e	i	a	h	w
p	o	e	m	c	u	a	d	v	i	c	e	f
o	o	t	o	a	s	p	i	c	e	e	n	a
t	d	J	a	n	u	a	r	y	a	x	f	c
w	h	o	p	l	y	v	o	i	c	e	b	e

Spelling Sums

11. Find list or revision words.

(a) **be + cause** = ⬚⬚⬚

(b) **sw + eep** = ⬚⬚⬚

(c) **tr + ace** = ⬚⬚⬚

(d) **pl + ace** = ⬚⬚⬚

(e) **m + ice** = ⬚⬚⬚

(f) **sp + ark** = ⬚⬚⬚

Spelling Patterns

12. Use the correct colour for these words.

(a) Colour the '**ace**' words yellow.

(b) Colour the '**ice**' words blue.

(c) Colour the other words red.

who	voice
disgrace	advice
trace	January

Additional Activities

13. (a) Write two more '**ace**' words and two more '**ice**' words. Check your spelling.

(b) Use a dictionary to write a definition for each of your new '**ace**' and '**ice**' words.

(c) Write four sentences, each containing one of your new '**ace**' and '**ice**' words.

Unit 11

Look

Say

Trace

Cover

Write

Check

List Words	Practise	Practise	T	D
page				
huge				
stage				
cage				
bandage				
bridge				
badge				
hedge				
judge				
bench				
branch				
crunch				
wrench				
match				
watch				
catch				
please				
February				

Missing Letters

More Missing Letters

1. Add '**ge**' or '**dge**' to make list words.

(a) bri _____

(b) hu _____

(c) pa _____

(d) ba _____

(e) he _____

(f) banda _____

2. Add '**ch**' or '**tch**' to make list words.

(a) ben _____

(b) ca _____

(c) wa _____

(d) crun _____

(e) wren _____

(f) bran _____

ge dge ch tch

Crossword

3. Use list words to solve the crossword.

Across

4. Bushes that can make a fence.
5. A sudden twist or pull.
8. A packet of crisps, _____.
11. Material for a wound.
12. My mum's shoes and bag always _____.
14. The leaf of a book.
15. He had to _____ the singing competition.
16. Vast, gigantic or enormous.

Down

1. It can be built over a river.
2. The parrot often came out of its _____.
3. A long seat.
5. It tells you the time.
6. To crush with the teeth.
7. Part of a tree.
9. Actors perform on a _____.
10. The shortest month of the year.
11. We have a _____ on our blazer.
13. To take hold or seize.

Plurals

4. Add 's' or 'es' to make the list words plural.

(a) page _____

(b) match _____

(c) badge _____

(d) branch _____

(e) bridge _____

(f) bandage _____

Alphabetical Order

5. Write these words in alphabetical order.

| huge | cage | watch |
| stage | | bench |

_____

_____

_____

_____

_____

Unit 11

ge dge ch tch

List Words

page
huge
stage
cage
bandage
bridge
badge
hedge
judge
bench
branch
crunch
wrench
match
watch
catch
please
February

Revision Words

spent
rent
went
grant
camp
bump
some
their

Compound Words

6. Write a list or revision word that can be added to make a compound word.

(a) _____ dog

(b) _____ site

(c) _____ mark

(d) bird _____

(e) _____ where

(f) _____ phrase

Small Words

7. Find small words in these list or revision words.

(a) branch

(b) hedge

(c) badge

(d) bridge

(e) crunch

(f) match

Synonyms

8. Find a list or revision word with a similar meaning.

(a) enormous _____

(b) hire _____

(c) referee _____

(d) knock _____

(e) spanner _____

(f) allow _____

Two Meanings

9. The word 'watch' has two meanings. One has been drawn. Draw another meaning.

Word Search

10. Find the list and revision words in the word search.

page	badge	wrench
huge	hedge	match
stage	judge	watch
cage	bench	catch
bandage	branch	please
bridge	crunch	February
spent	went	rent
grant	camp	bump
some	their	

o	w	a	t	c	h	q	s	p	e	n	t	r
a	b	u	m	p	u	r	i	j	u	d	g	e
k	b	r	a	n	c	h	p	a	g	e	x	n
w	m	a	t	c	h	e	d	g	e	d	f	t
y	d	b	a	n	d	a	g	e	l	i	s	c
e	d	e	F	e	b	r	u	a	r	y	a	a
s	j	n	r	w	e	n	t	i	b	h	w	m
t	y	c	z	x	c	a	g	e	a	r	r	p
a	t	h	e	i	r	b	r	i	d	g	e	f
g	x	z	r	s	h	u	g	e	g	c	n	w
e	p	c	a	t	c	h	o	o	e	v	c	x
p	l	e	a	s	e	g	r	a	n	t	h	e
s	o	m	e	d	c	r	u	n	c	h	m	f

Missing Words

11. Complete the sentences using these list or revision words.

bench   watch   huge   please   February   match   spent   their

(a) The children were crying because _____ bikes had been stolen.

(b) May I have a biscuit, _____?

(c) We will sit on the _____ and _____ the _____.

(d) There are 28 days in _____ and 29 days in a leap year.

(e) I _____ all my money on a _____ ice-cream.

Additional Activities

12. (a) Write six more months of the year. Check your spelling.

(b) Write your new month words in alphabetical order.

(c) For each month word, write an event that usually occurs during that month.

Unit 12

 Look

 Say

 Trace

 Write

 Check

List Words	Practise	Practise	T	D
yourself				
himself				
herself				
myself				
outside				
inside				
offside				
seaside				
someone				
something				
sometimes				
somebody				
everyone				
everything				
everybody				
everywhere				
centimetre				
metre				

Compound Words

1. Draw lines to make compound words.

(a) every — side

(b) sea — times

(c) him — body

(d) some — self

Letters into Words

2. Write three list words using the letters in the hearts. (Letters can be used more than once.)

Hearts: s, e, i, a, d, c, n, r, o, f, t

Compound Words

Crossword

3. Use list words to solve the crossword.

Across

1. Someone.
6. Somebody.
7. 100 centimetres.
10. You.
12. All things.
14. Interior.
17. Now and then.
18. Opposite of 'himself'.

Down

2. Opposite of 'inside'.
3. Every person.
4. A metric unit of length.
5. An unknown thing.
8. All the people.
9. The football player was ____.
11. In all places.
13. Opposite of 'herself'.
15. Me.
16. A beach area.

Small Words

4. Write the list words that contain these small words.

(a) as _____

(b) our _____

(c) cent _____

(d) of _____

(e) here _____

Me!

Unit 12

List Words

yourself
himself
herself
myself
outside
inside
offside
seaside
someone
something
sometimes
somebody
everyone
everything
everybody
everywhere
centimetre
metre

Revision Words

meat
teach
dear
hear
keep
sleep
would
pupil

Word Hunt

5. (a) Which list words have a 'th' sound?

[_____] [_____]

(b) Which revision word is part of an eye? [_____]

(c) Which list word is used in football? [_____]

(d) Which list and revision words contain a double letter?

[_____] [_____] [_____]

All Mixed Up

6. Unjumble these list and revision words.

(a) siiden _____ (b) dare _____

(c) uroslyfe _____ (d) olwud _____

(e) esiased _____ (f) terem _____

Missing Words

7. Complete the sentences using list or revision words.

(a) _____ I'm allowed to stay up late.

(b) Can you _____ me to skate?

(c) Come _____ out of the rain.

(d) Put the baby to bed for a _____.

Read and Draw

8. (a) Yourself at the seaside

(b) Someone eating a meat pie

Word Search

9. Find the list and revision words in the word search.

u	f	e	s	o	m	e	b	o	d	y	p	r	l	t
e	s	o	m	e	t	i	m	e	s	l	m	o	r	w
w	e	v	e	r	y	w	h	e	r	e	e	t	h	e
q	e	v	e	r	y	t	h	i	n	g	t	u	i	v
b	e	h	e	r	s	e	l	f	i	a	r	e	m	e
s	m	e	p	o	w	o	u	l	d	v	e	d	s	r
o	e	p	u	p	i	l	s	e	a	s	i	d	e	y
m	a	o	g	y	i	n	s	i	d	e	h	k	l	o
e	t	x	a	m	y	s	e	l	f	o	e	e	f	n
t	s	o	u	t	s	i	d	e	t	b	a	e	i	e
h	e	y	o	u	r	s	e	l	f	r	r	p	t	s
i	o	d	b	e	v	e	r	y	b	o	d	y	e	l
n	c	e	n	t	i	m	e	t	r	e	f	n	a	e
g	p	a	s	o	m	e	o	n	e	g	d	w	c	e
f	i	r	s	o	f	f	s	i	d	e	r	t	h	p

yourself   offside
everyone   himself
seaside   everything
herself   someone
everybody   myself
something   everywhere
outside   sometimes
centimetre   inside
somebody   metre
meat   teach
dear   hear
keep   sleep
would   pupil

Shape Sorter

10. Write the word that fits in each shape.

(a)   (b)   (c)

Word Worm

11. Circle each list or revision word you can find in the word worm.

heareverywhereyourselfmeatmyselfherself

Additional Activities

12. (a) Write five more compound words. Check your spelling.

(b) Write your five new compound words in alphabetical order.

(c) Write five sentences each containing one of your new compound words.

Unit 13

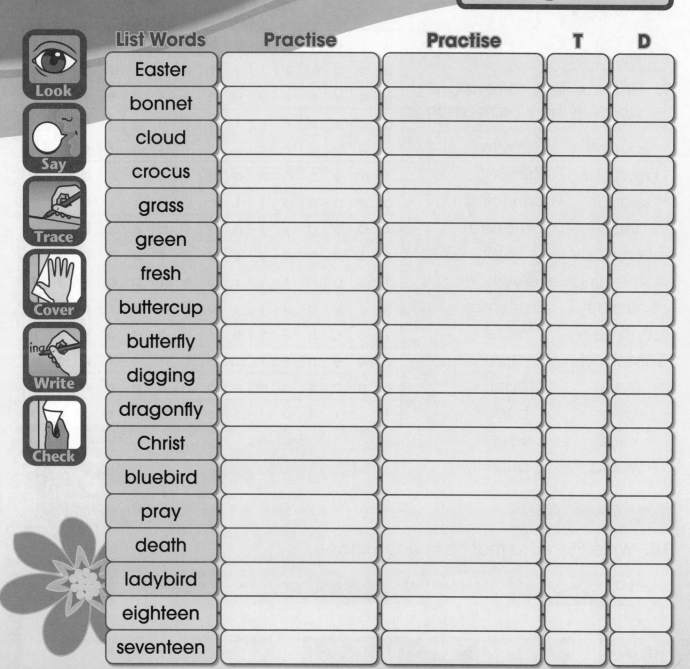

List Words	Practise	Practise	T	D
Easter				
bonnet				
cloud				
crocus				
grass				
green				
fresh				
buttercup				
butterfly				
digging				
dragonfly				
Christ				
bluebird				
pray				
death				
ladybird				
eighteen				
seventeen				

Look **Say** **Trace** **Cover** **Write** **Check**

Small Words

1. Write the list word that contains these small words.

   (a) on
   (b) at
   (c) us
   (d) is
   (e) as

All Mixed Up

2. Unjumble these list words.

   (a) hrfes _____
   (b) ryap _____
   (c) oclud _____
   (d) rladidby _____
   (e) nevetenes _____
   (f) berlidub _____

Spring/Easter

Crossword

3. Use list words to solve the crossword.

Across

2. Small songbird.
5. The opposite of 'birth'.
7. At church, we _____ together.
9. Yellow flower.
11. The fruit is _____, not tinned.
12. Can bring rain.
13. Similar to a moth.
15. He had a spade and was _____ in the garden.
17. Three less than twenty.

Down

1. The colour of grass.
2. A head covering.
3. Has long lacy wings.
4. Red with black dots.
6. The name for Jesus.
8. Time when Christians celebrate the rising of Christ.
10. Small flower.
14. Two greater than sixteen.
16. Lawn.

Secret Words

4. (a) Take '**Ea**' off '**Easter**' and put in '**ham**'. _____

   (b) Take '**bird**' off '**bluebird**' and put in '**bell**'. _____

   (c) Take '**teen**' off '**seventeen**' and put in '**th**'. _____

   (d) Take '**cl**' off '**cloud**' and put in '**pr**'.

Unit 13

List Words

Easter
bonnet
cloud
crocus
grass
green
fresh
buttercup
butterfly
digging
dragonfly
Christ
bluebird
pray
death
ladybird
eighteen
seventeen

Compound Words

5. Match the words to make compound words.

(a) dragon — drop

(b) butter — bird

(c) rain — fly

(d) blue — cup

Mixed-up Sentences

6. Unjumble these sentences and write them correctly.

(a) on ladybird crocus. The sipped the raindrop the

_____

(b) Monday bonnets. we On thirteen made Easter

_____

Changing Words

7. Change one letter in each word to make a list or revision word.

(a) warp _____   (b) casket _____

(c) glass _____   (d) flesh _____

Revision Words

flower
bunny
basket
warm
raindrop
spring
thirteen
Monday

Word Worm

8. Circle each list or revision word you can find in the word worm.

diggingprayMondayfreshbonnetEaster

Spring/Easter

Word Search

9. Find the list and revision words in the Easter egg word search.

Easter bonnet
cloud crocus
grass green
fresh buttercup
butterfly
digging
dragonfly
Christ
bluebird
pray
death
ladybird seventeen
eighteen flower
bunny basket
warm raindrop
spring thirteen
Monday

```
            c v s z l
          b y r m e d a t q
          g o v o q v r d h q e
        v r n p c b e a y i k g j
      n l a n r u f n g b r j h r b
      m g s e a s c t o i t b x y g
    p n n s t y g l e n r e g c r y h
    b l u e b i r d o e f d e r w j l f z
    y d i g g i n g u n l x n e q j r h m
    e e s p r i n g d q y f r e s h E d g
    i x b u t t e r c u p z o n l e a b w
    l y w n y o e i g h t e e n s d s z y
    q g p o m b u t t e r f l y e t h
    r a i n d r o p t s u r t a e
    b a s k e t j j b u n n y t r
    f l o w e r r k l u i n h
    M o n d a y w o w r w
    C h r i s t x s m
    w a r m m
```

Word Hunt

10. (a) Which three words are insects?

[ ] [ ] [ ]

(b) Which three words are numbers?

[ ] [ ] [ ]

[ ]

(c) Which word rhymes with '**focus**'?

Additional Activities

11. (a) Write six more Easter or spring words. Check your spelling.

(b) Write an Easter message.

(c) Find and write six more compound words.

Look **Say** **Trace** **Cover** **Write** **Check**

List Words	Practise	Practise	T	D
weren't				
I'd				
won't				
we've				
they've				
what's				
that's				
there's				
you're				
hasn't				
you've				
we're				
she's				
you'll				
they'd				
they're				
Wales				
Scotland				

Word Hunt

1. Which list word(s)

(a) begins with 'h'?

(b) have the letters 've'?

(c) have the contraction of the word 'not' in them?

(d) are countries?

(e) has the smallest number of letters?

Contractions

Crossword

2. Use list words to solve the crossword.

Across
2. Short for has not.
3. Short for we are.
5. Short for she is.
6. Short for that is.
10. Short for there is.
11. Short for you will or shall.
12. Short for you have.
14. Short for they are.
15. Short for they had or would.

Down
1. Cardiff is its capital city.
3. Short for what is.
4. Edinburgh is its capital city.
7. Short for were not.
8. Short for we have
9. Short for will not.
12. Short for you are.
13. Short for they have.

Changing Words

3. Change one letter in each word to make a list word.

(a) they've _____
(b) she'd _____
(c) you're _____
(d) walks _____

Letters into Words

4. Write four list words using the letters in the stars. (Letters can be used more than once.)

r v '
y h t
e s d

Unit 14

List Words

weren't
I'd
won't
we've
they've
what's
that's
there's
you're
hasn't
you've
we're
she's
you'll
they'd
they're
Wales
Scotland

Revision Words

bang
along
belong
thing
being
hung
old
has

Contractions

5. Write the contractions.

(a) you will _____   (b) she is _____

(c) what is _____   (d) I had _____

(e) they are _____   (f) will not _____

(g) we are _____   (h) there is _____

Missing Words

6. Complete the sentences using list or revision words.

(a) Walk carefully _____ the wall.

(b) Susan is sick, so _____ not been at school.

(c) My friends are happy, as _____ all going to the circus.

(d) _____ not fair, I didn't break the window!

Alphabetical Order

7. Write these list and revision words in alphabetical order.

you're   Scotland
what's   that's
old

_____

_____

_____

_____

_____

All Mixed Up

8. Unjumble these list and revision words. Use a coloured pencil to place the apostrophe in the words.

(a) uyero _____

(b) gunh _____

(c) veew _____

(d) hatts _____

(e) deyht _____

(f) legonb _____

Contractions

9. Find the list and revision words in the word search.

weren't   that's   she's
I'd   there's   they'd
won't   you're   Wales
we've   hasn't   Scotland
they've   you've   belong
what's   we're   hung
bang   along   has
thing   being   old
you'll   they're

t	h	e	y	'v	e	y	o	h	u	n	g	n
h	l	k	o	m	w	e	r	e	n	't	e	w
i	y	o	u	'r	e	t	a	S	s	h	e	's
n	s	b	'l	a	i	h	P	c	t	S	c	o
g	h	e	l	l	t	e	w	o	n	't	s	t
d	e	i	b	o	h	y	p	t	o	l	d	h
l	'd	n	a	n	a	'r	s	l	r	e	n	e
w	t	g	a	g	t	e	h	a	s	n	't	y
e	h	h	l	w	's	b	a	n	g	c	o	'd
'v	W	a	l	e	s	W	a	d	s	l	a	n
e	o	s	g	'r	p	f	v	w	h	a	t	's
c	g	h	b	e	l	o	n	g	v	e	u	w
y	o	u	'v	e	g	b	t	h	e	r	e	's

10. Write a list or revision word that fits in each shape.

(a)

(b)

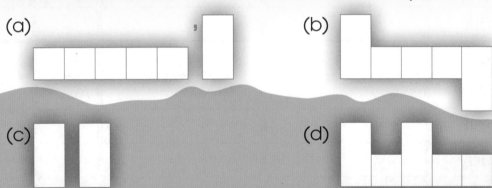

(c)

(d)

11. Circle each list or revision word you can find in the word worm.

bangwe'rel'dScotlandthey'realong

12. (a) Write three more contractions. Check your spelling.

    (b) Write your three new contractions in their full form; e.g. '**they've**' — '**they have**'.

    (c) Write three sentences, each containing one of your new words.

Unit 15

aw oa ore a

Look

Say

Trace

Cover

Write

Check

List Words	Practise	Practise	T	D
draw				
straw				
law				
claw				
soar				
board				
oar				
roar				
sore				
tore				
more				
score				
stalk				
walk				
talk				
chalk				
today				
year				

Homophones

1. The list words '**sore**' and '**soar**' are homophones. '**Soar**' means to glide high.

   (a) Write a definition for '**sore**'.

   _____

   (b) Write a sentence using '**sore**'.

   _____

What am I?

2. (a) You must obey me.
   There are different kinds.
   There is a price to pay if you break me.

   I am the [_____].

   (b) I am usually long and thin.
   I am sometimes coloured.
   I am used for writing or drawing.

   I am [_____].

My Spelling Workbook C—Prim-Ed Publishing—www.prim-ed.com

Crossword

3. Use list words to solve the crossword.

Across

2. Extra
3. Curved nail of an animal.
4. The rules of a country.
7. Use the power of speech.
9. Long, thin, flat piece of wood.
10. She _____ open the present.
12. Number of goals.
13. 365 days.
14. Fly high into the air.

Down

1. Make a picture.
3. Use it to write on a blackboard.
5. Go on foot.
6. Painful or aching.
7. The day after yesterday.
8. The _____ of a lion is very loud.
11. You use it to row a boat.
12. A thin, hollow tube used for drinking.
14. The stem of a plant.

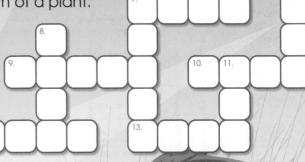

Spelling Patterns

4. Use the correct colour for these words.

(a) Colour the '**aw**' words red.

(b) Colour the '**oa**' words blue.

(c) Colour the '**ore**' words green.

board	score
claw	roar
more	scrap

Unit 15

List Words

- draw
- straw
- law
- claw
- soar
- board
- oar
- roar
- sore
- tore
- more
- score
- stalk
- walk
- talk
- chalk
- today
- year

Revision Words

- away
- day
- stay
- tail
- wait
- train
- Tuesday
- Wednesday

All Mixed Up

5. Unjumble these list words.

(a) eary _____   (b) kalt _____

(c) taswr _____   (d) emor _____

(e) oecsr _____   (f) ritan _____

(g) tiwa _____   (h) skalt _____

Suffixes

6. Add the suffixes 'ed', 'ing' or 'er' to make new words.

	'ed'	'ing'	'er'
walk			
board			
talk			
wait			

Compound Words

7. Write a list or revision word to make these compound words.

(a) _____ light   (b) _____ berry

(c) _____ back   (d) over _____

(e) _____ way   (f) _____ bridge

Missing Words

8. Complete the sentences using list or revision words.

(a) Watch the plane _____ into the sky.

(b) Who do you think will _____ the first goal?

(c) _____ here until the _____ has moved down the track.

(d) Please may I have some _____ milk?

Word Search

9. Find the list and revision words in the word search.

draw	oar	stalk
straw	roar	walk
law	sore	talk
claw	tore	chalk
soar	more	today
board	score	year
away	day	stay
tail	wait	train
Tuesday	Wednesday	

s	j	t	w	a	l	k	z	f	l	u	z	s
c	b	o	a	r	d	t	m	p	a	m	t	t
o	q	r	t	c	l	a	w	n	j	o	a	a
r	h	e	T	v	a	m	c	v	t	r	l	l
e	g	o	u	w	w	q	h	r	r	e	k	k
c	q	a	e	o	d	t	a	m	a	o	t	s
g	k	r	s	c	r	a	l	s	i	n	w	o
s	r	a	d	r	a	i	k	t	n	o	y	r
t	o	d	a	y	w	l	i	s	o	a	r	e
a	r	i	y	a	w	a	y	s	y	e	a	r
y	o	q	x	a	d	a	y	r	l	q	g	f
w	a	i	t	l	m	s	t	r	a	w	b	y
m	r	W	e	d	n	e	s	d	a	y	y	m

Missing Letters

10. Add the correct letters to complete the list or revision words.

(a) dr _ _ _   (b) st _ _ _

(c) t _ _ l   (d) _ _ _ r

(e) to _ _ _ _   (f) Wed _ _ _ _ day

(g) t _ lk   (h) w _ _ _ t

Word Meanings

11. Draw lines to match the words to their meanings.

(a) tore

(b) stay

(c) stalk

(d) board

stop

stem

get on

ripped

Additional Activities

12. (a) 'Today' and 'year' are time words. Write four more time words. Check your spelling.

(b) Use a dictionary to write a definition for each of your new time words.

(c) Write four sentences, each containing one of your new time words.

Unit 16

Look

Say

Trace

Cover

Write

Check

List Words	Practise	Practise	T	D
war				
warrior				
warp				
warning				
ward				
wardrobe				
warn				
warmth				
swarm				
dwarf				
award				
warden				
towards				
warren				
reward				
warlock				
fortnight				
second				

Small Words

1. Write the list words that contain these small words.

(a) or _____ _____

(b) arm _____ _____

(c) rob _____

(d) on _____

(e) den _____

(f) in _____

What am I?

2. (a) I am a man.
I often wear unusual clothes.
I cast spells.

I am a _____ .

(b) I am brave.
I fight with the enemy.
I carry weapons.

I am a _____ .

My Spelling Workbook C—Prim-Ed Publishing—www.prim-ed.com

war

Crossword

3. Use list words to solve the crossword.

Across

1. Rabbits live here underground.
3. A fighting man.
4. A male witch.
6. Two weeks.
8. To advise, urge or inform.
9. She was in _____ 7 at the hospital.
10. There was a storm _____ before the storm.
11. After the first.
13. A group of bees and their queen.
15. To become twisted or out of shape.

Down

2. He got a _____ for finding the wallet.
3. A tall cupboard for hanging clothes.
5. A traffic _____.
7. In the direction of.
10. Heat.
12. Happy or Grumpy or Doc.
14. A prize or trophy.
15. How long did the 2nd World _____ last?

Compound Words

4. Draw lines to make compound words.

(a) fort · · lock

(b) ward · · night

(c) war · · robe

Letters into Words

5. Write six list words using the letters in the stars. (Letters can be used more than once.)

d a w
p n r
d f

Unit 16

List Words

war
warrior
warp
warning
ward
wardrobe
warn
warmth
swarm
dwarf
award
warden
towards
warren
reward
warlock
fortnight
second

Revision Words

girl
first
hurt
turn
never
over
Thursday
Friday

Mixed-up Sentences

6. Unjumble the sentences.

(a) before. girl of never seen had a swarm The bees

_____

(b) was an time fortnight. given a for He award second in the

_____

Antonyms

7. Write a list or revision word with the opposite meaning.

(a) punishment ⬚⬚⬚⬚ (b) giant ⬚⬚⬚⬚

(c) coolness ⬚⬚⬚⬚ (d) often ⬚⬚⬚⬚

(e) peace ⬚⬚⬚⬚ (f) boy ⬚⬚⬚⬚

Missing Letters

8. Add the correct letters to complete the list or revision words.

(a) __ h __ r __ __ ay (b) f __ __ __ n __ __ __ t

(c) __ e __ er (d) s __ c __ __ d

Read and Draw

9. (a) A warlock casting a spell

(b) A swarm of bees chasing a dwarf

war

Word Search

10. Find the list and revision words in the word search.

war	warn	towards
warrior	warmth	warren
warp	swarm	reward
warning	dwarf	warlock
ward	award	fortnight
wardrobe	warden	second
girl	first	hurt
turn	never	over
Thursday	Friday	

a	w	a	r	d	e	n	i	f	w	a	r	d
w	p	w	f	o	r	t	n	i	g	h	t	F
a	w	a	r	r	e	n	n	e	v	e	r	r
r	p	t	f	i	r	s	t	w	a	r	n	i
d	r	o	w	w	a	r	p	w	t	t	v	d
w	e	w	a	d	y	s	w	a	r	m	p	a
w	w	a	r	w	T	h	u	r	s	d	a	y
a	a	r	r	a	v	h	x	d	g	i	r	l
r	r	d	i	r	x	a	y	r	q	p	u	y
n	d	s	o	f	j	f	b	o	h	u	r	t
i	w	a	r	l	o	c	k	b	t	u	r	n
n	k	o	v	e	r	o	s	e	c	o	n	d
g	w	a	r	w	w	a	r	m	t	h	s	n

Spelling Sums

11. Find list or revision words.

(a) **ward + robe** = _____

(b) **Fri + day** = _____

(c) **re + ward** = _____

(d) **war + rior** = _____

(e) **fir + st** = _____

(f) **warm + th** = _____

Synonyms

12. Find a list or revision word with a similar meaning.

(a) fighter [ ]

(b) twist [ ]

(c) harm [ ]

(d) burrow [ ]

(e) prize [ ]

Additional Activities

13. (a) '**Second**' is an ordinal number. Use a dictionary to write a definition of an ordinal number.

(b) Write four more ordinal numbers. Check your spelling.

(c) Write four sentences, each containing one of your new ordinal number words.

Unit 17

Look

Say

Trace

Cover

Write

Check

List Words	Practise	Practise	T	D
comb				
lamb				
dumb				
numb				
crumb				
wrap				
wreck				
write				
wrong				
honest				
ghost				
hour				
know				
knight				
knife				
knot				
tomorrow				
England				

Silent Letters

1. Sort the list words into family groups.

(a) Silent b

(b) Silent w

(c) Silent h

(d) Silent k

Silent Letters

Crossword

2. Use list words to solve the crossword.

Across

2. To cover something.
4. It cuts.
6. The day after today.
10. It was so cold my toes were _____!
12. Opposite of 'right'.
13. Make a _____ in your tie.
14. A young sheep.
15. I _____ how to swim.
17. It rhymes with 'toast'.
18. Unable to speak.

Down

1. Mark something down on paper.
3. He was a _____ in shining armour.
5. A very small bit of biscuit or bread.
7. The divers found a ship_____.
8. 60 minutes.
9. London is its capital city.
11. Truthful.
16. A brush and _____.

DRESS-UP DAY!

What am I?

3. (a) I am less than a day.

I am more than a second.

There are 60 minutes in me.

I am an _____.

(b) I have teeth.

I am used daily.

I help to make you look tidy.

I am a _____.

Unit 17

List Words

comb
lamb
dumb
numb
crumb
wrap
wreck
write
wrong
honest
ghost
hour
know
knight
knife
knot
tomorrow
England

Revision Words

loaf
float
soap
below
own
crow
Saturday
Sunday

Proofreading

4. A list or revision word has been incorrectly spelt in each sentence. Circle it and write it correctly on the line.

(a) There was not a crum left on the plate.

(b) I am going to a football match on Saterday.

(c) Rap your lunch in cling film.

(d) If you're honist you tell the truth.

(e) Wash your hands with sope and water.

(f) I no the answer to that question.

Word Hunt

5. Which list or revision word(s):

(a) has London as its capital city?

(b) has the least letters?

(c) are at the weekend?

(d) means 'can't speak'?

(e) is a spirit?

Changing Words

6. Change one letter in each word to make a list or revision word.

(a) trap _____

(b) soup _____

(c) bomb _____

(d) lame _____

(e) owe _____

(f) wring _____

(g) grow _____

(h) pour _____

My Spelling Workbook C—Prim-Ed Publishing—www.prim-ed.com

Silent Letters

Word Search

7. Find the list and revision words in the word search.

comb	wreck	know
lamb	write	knight
dumb	wrong	knife
numb	honest	knot
crumb	ghost	tomorrow
wrap	hour	England
loaf	float	soap
below	own	crow
Saturday	Sunday	

t	f	j	S	a	t	u	r	d	a	y	d	u
k	l	k	f	d	y	c	r	u	m	b	u	c
h	o	n	e	s	t	y	e	r	l	a	m	b
z	a	i	l	h	n	i	l	o	a	f	b	p
w	t	f	s	c	k	b	t	z	w	r	n	t
r	S	e	g	o	n	e	o	l	r	E	u	c
e	u	s	h	m	o	l	m	b	i	n	m	r
c	n	t	o	b	w	o	o	m	t	g	b	o
k	d	o	s	o	o	w	r	f	e	l	v	w
n	a	w	t	f	w	i	r	s	o	a	p	k
a	y	n	t	a	w	r	o	n	g	n	x	n
t	w	r	a	p	e	p	w	p	u	d	l	o
k	n	i	g	h	t	h	o	u	r	c	o	t

Hair salon

Rhyming Words

8. Choose a rhyming word from the list or revision words.

(a) boat _____   (b) roast _____

(c) strap _____   (d) song _____

(e) life _____   (f) bone _____

Homophones

Homophones are words that are pronounced the same but have a different meaning and spelling.

9. Can you find the homophone to match these words?

(a) night _____

(b) not _____

(c) right _____

(d) no _____

Additional Activities

10. (a) 'England' is the name of a country. Write five more country names. Check your spelling.

(b) Write the capital city of each of your new countries in a sentence; e.g. 'London is the capital city of England'.

Unit 18

Look
Say
Trace
Cover
Write
Check

List Words	Practise	Practise	T	D
plane				
atlas				
boat				
crab				
passport				
rock				
flipflops				
beach				
flight				
ticket				
runway				
landing				
pool				
hotel				
salty				
uniform				
said				
there				

Secret Words

1. (a) Change 'pass' to 're' in 'passport'. _____

   (b) Change 'run' to 'high' in 'runway'. _____

   (c) Take 'b' from 'beach' and put in 't'. _____

   (d) Change 'uni' to 'per' in 'uniform'. _____

Synonyms

2. Find list words with similar meanings.

   (a) identification _____   (b) pond _____

   (c) ship _____   (d) airstrip _____

   (e) seashore _____   (f) boulder _____

Summer Holidays

Crossword

3. Use list words to solve the crossword.

Across

3. The teacher _____, 'Be quiet'.
6. Has a hard shell.
7. A hard mineral material of the earth's crust.
8. Landing strip.
9. Footwear.
12. Book me a room at the _____.
14. It floats.
15. You need this when you travel abroad.

Down

1. A soldier's clothing.
2. A book of maps.
3. You cannot drink sea water as it is _____.
4. Needed to get on a plane.
5. The plane will be _____ at 3 o'clock.
10. A journey made in an aircraft.
11. 'Aero_____'.
13. In or at that place.
14. Seaside.
16. A pond; puddle.

Secret Code

4. Use the secret code to find the summer message.

a	b	c	d	e	f	g	h	i	l	m	n	o	p	r	s	t	w
1	2	3	4	5	6	7	8	9	10	11	12	13	14	15	16	17	18

___ ___ ___ ___   ___ ___ ___ ___ ___ ___ ___ ___   ___ ___   ___ ___ ___   ___ ___ ___ ___ ___
(18) (5) (1) (15)   (6) (10) (9) (14) (6) (10) (13) (14) (16)   (13) (12)   (17) (8) (5)   (2) (5) (1) (3) (8)

Unit 18

List Words

plane
atlas
boat
crab
passport
rock
flipflops
beach
flight
ticket
runway
landing
pool
hotel
salty
uniform
said
there

Revision Words

bucket
spade
wave
site
seagull
seaweed
number
him

Proofreading

5. Circle the incorrect words and rewrite them correctly in the spaces.

(a) The plain landed on the beech.

_____ _____

(b) Their is a krab in the swimming pole.

_____ _____

Read and Draw

6. He is at the beach with a bucket and spade.

Changing Words

7. Change one letter in each word to make a list or revision word.

(a) these _____
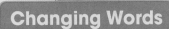
(b) plate _____

(c) cram _____
(d) rook _____

(e) maid _____
(f) lending _____

Compound Words

8. Match the words to make compound words.

(a) run — port

(b) sea — flops

(c) pass — way

(d) flip — gull

Word Search

9. Find the list and revision words in the word search.

plane   atlas
boat   crab
passport   rock
flipflops beach
flight   ticket
runway   landing
pool   hotel
salty   uniform
said   there
bucket   spade
wave   site
seagull
seaweed
him
number

					c	r	a	b			
				v	s	f	l	i	g	h	t
			s	e	a	g	u	l	l	j	r
			q	f	l	i	p	f	l	o	p	s
w	x	x		v	t	t	b	m	d	z	m	h	w
p	a	s	s	p	o	r	t	y	g	k	z	j	m	h	h
v	i	w	o	l	o	i	n	p	g	z	j	j	i	v
e	z	q	o	a	c	s	e	a	w	e	e	d	m
s	v	w	e	l	n	k	p	l	a	n	e	p
r	s	p	a	d	e	h	g	q	l	k	y
	a	b	i	s	r	u	n	w	a	y
	e	t	u	n	i	f	o	r	m	m	k
	j	g	l	w	g	n	u	m	b	e	r	d
w	b	e	a	c	h	r	r	f	w	c	b	r
b	t	j	z	s	h	o	t	e	l	m	a	h	t
t	h	e	r	e	q	r	b	u	c	k	e	t	e	h
m	n	r	w	r	t	i	c	k	e	t	v	d	z	t
s	i	t	e	f	o	f	a	v	k	x	l	y
x	f	k	y	b	o	a	t
s	a	i	d	k

More Than One

10. Add 's' or 'es' to make more than one.

(a) beach _____   (b) number _____

(c) atlas _____   (d) plane _____

(e) wave _____   (f) site _____

Additional Activities

11. (a) Write six more 'summer holiday' words. Check your spelling.

(b) Write your new words in alphabetical order.

(c) Write a holiday postcard to your friend. Use all six of your new words.

Difficult Words I Have Found

Word	Practise	Practise	Practise

My Spelling Workbook C—Prim-Ed Publishing—www.prim-ed.com

My Spelling Dictionary Aa to Ff

Aa

Bb

Cc

Dd

Ee

Ff

Gg

Hh

Ii

Jj

Kk

Ll

My Spelling Workbook C—Prim-Ed Publishing—www.prim-ed.com

Mm

Nn

Oo

Pp

Qq

Rr

Ss

My Spelling Dictionary Tt to Zz

Tt

Uu

Vv

Ww

Xx

Yy

Zz

My Spelling Workbook C—Prim-Ed Publishing—www.prim-ed.com